Brain Teasers

HEAD-SCRATCHING PUZZLE CHALLENGES!

ARCTURUS

ARCTURUS

This edition published in 2013 by Arcturus Publishing Limited
26/27 Bickels Yard, 151–153 Bermondsey Street,
London SE1 3HA

ISBN: 978-1-84858-071-8
CH001961US
Supplier 16, Date 1212, Print run 2321

Text and illustrations by Small World Design

Printed in Singapore

Fishy friend

Break the code by seeing which number relates to which letter
and reveal what type of fish this is.

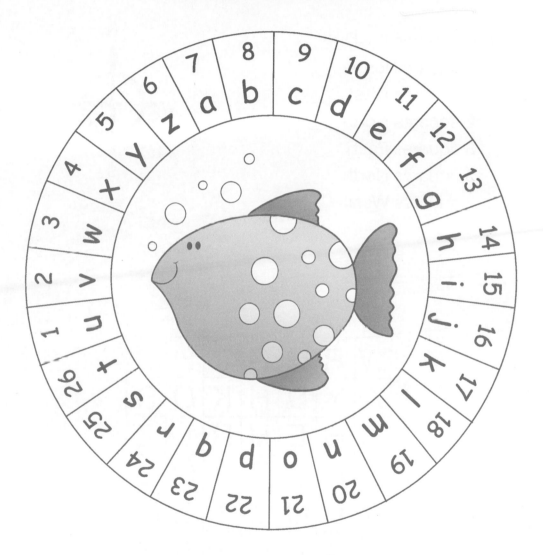

‾‾ ‾‾ ‾‾ ‾‾ ‾‾ ‾‾ ‾‾
14 11 24 24 15 20 13

Natural beauty

Starting at the arrow, follow the compass clues
to reveal something pretty in the sky!

6 squares East   ___
1 square North   ___
5 squares West   ___
2 squares North ___
3 squares East   ___
3 squares North ___
3 squares West   ___

___ ___ ___ ___ ___ ___ ___

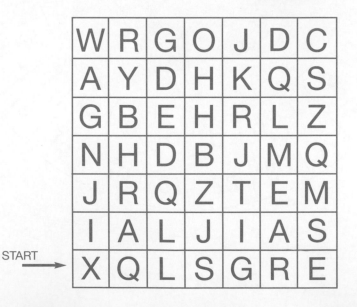

START →

W	R	G	O	J	D	C
A	Y	D	H	K	Q	S
G	B	E	H	R	L	Z
N	H	D	B	J	M	Q
J	R	Q	Z	T	E	M
I	A	L	J	I	A	S
X	Q	L	S	G	R	E

Count to 20

There are 5 pairs of numbers that add up to 20 in the grid.
Can you circle them?

3	19	1	15	2
16	4	8	10	4
11	2	10	10	2
4	15	5	8	5
10	3	4	14	6

Home, sweet home

Break the code to reveal the type of home this little bird is standing on.

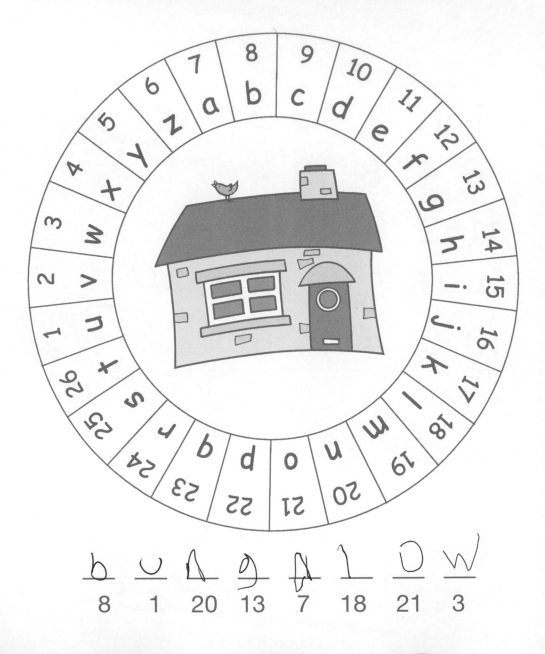

b u n g a l o w
8 1 20 13 7 18 21 3

Number count

Fill in the grid so that each row, column, and mini-square contains a number from 1 to 4.

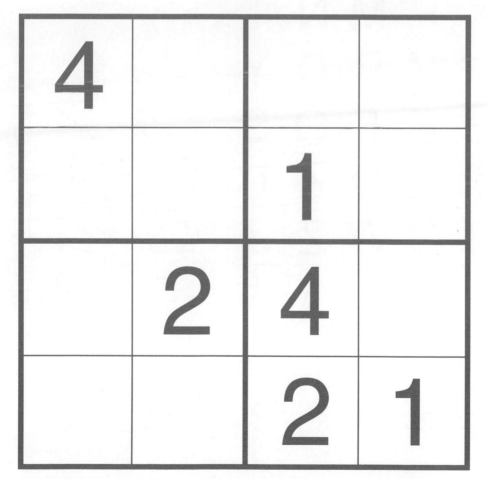

Letter pairs

In this grid, there are 5 pairs of letters that sit next to each other in the alphabet. Can you circle them?

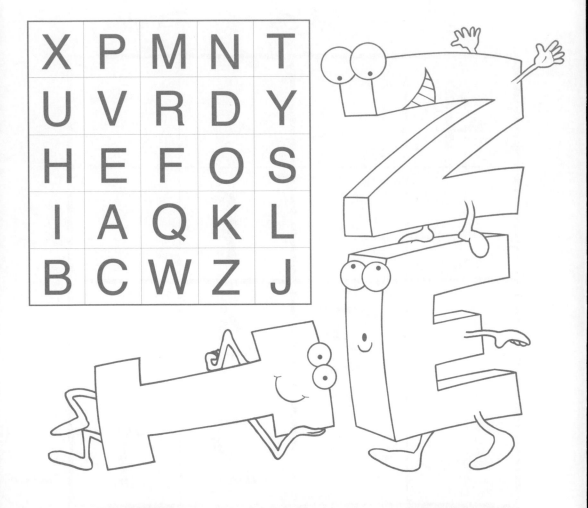

Yummy cake

Follow the trail and write down every second
letter to find a type of cake.

_ _ _ _ _ _ _

Number magic

Help this sniffer dog find the number sequences hidden in the grid.
Look up, down, across, and diagonally.

7398   5426   0095   3172   4401

9020   6394   1202   9980   0203

```
1 5 4 4 0 1 3 9 7 6
9 2 5 0 3 8 6 0 4 1
7 3 9 8 4 0 2 5 5 1
2 1 6 3 9 2 7 4 0 2
9 7 5 7 8 0 1 2 3 0
9 2 3 2 6 3 8 6 5 2
0 1 8 9 9 8 0 4 7 0
2 7 4 1 0 6 7 9 2 8
0 0 9 5 2 9 8 5 3 9
1 6 3 4 9 6 3 9 4 5
```

What's left?

Cross out 4 insects, 4 sea creatures, and 4 sports in the selection below.
What connects the remaining words?

STARFISH

SHARK

KATY

DRAGONFLY

WHALE

SEAL

WASP

RACHEL

KELLY

LADYBUG

BASEBALL

ANT

SOCCER

SWIMMING

HOCKEY

In the crowd

Study the boys in gym class and answer the questions below.

1. How many boys have only one arm in the air? _____

2. How many boys have their hands on their hips? _____

3. How many boys have their hands on their heads? _____

4. How many boys are doing a jumping jack? _____

5. How many boys are standing on one leg? _____

Destinations

Follow the trails to find out where the bags are headed.
Write the answers in the boxes.

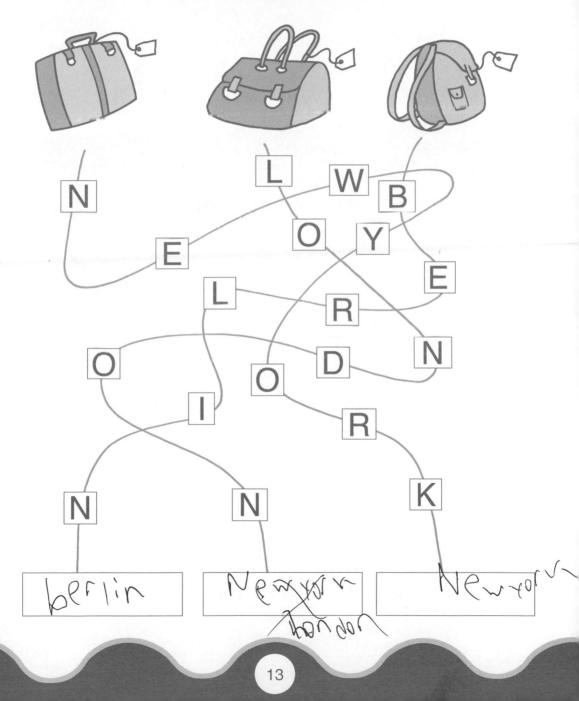

berlin

New york
london

New york

In the jungle

Follow the start arrow and the compass clues to find a jungle creature.

5 squares West ___
2 squares South ___
2 squares South ___
2 squares West ___
2 squares South ___
6 squares East ___

N

W   E

S

__ __ __ __ __ __

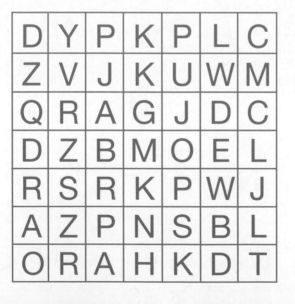

START ←

D	Y	P	K	P	L	C
Z	V	J	K	U	W	M
Q	R	A	G	J	D	C
D	Z	B	M	O	E	L
R	S	R	K	P	W	J
A	Z	P	N	S	B	L
O	R	A	H	K	D	T

Count to 30

There are 5 pairs of numbers that add up to 30 in the grid.
Can you circle them?

15	15	8	8	10
5	9	10	20	7
7	18	12	5	9
19	4	8	29	1
14	16	8	8	14

What's my name?

Who are these happy people? Follow the trails to spell out their names, then write them in the boxes.

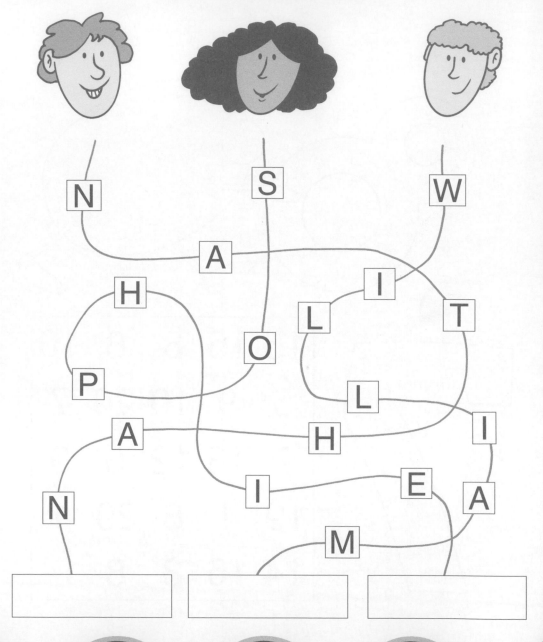

Sum it up

Fill in the grid so that each row, column, and
mini-square contains a number from 1 to 4.

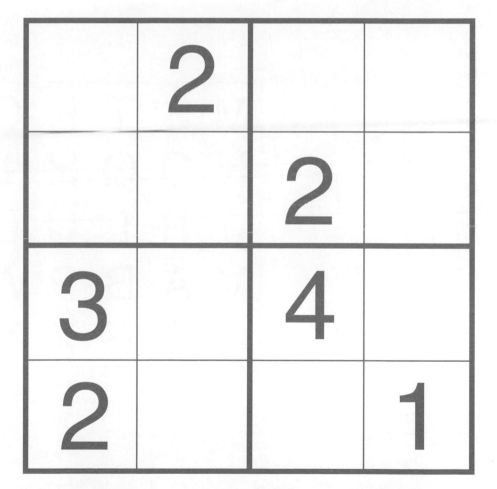

Perfect pairs

In this grid, there are 5 pairs of letters that sit next to each other in the alphabet. Can you circle them?

M	S	T	K	C
N	O	Q	H	I
J	R	L	U	E
V	A	B	P	W
D	G	F	X	Y

Wrap up warm!

Brrr! It's cold outside! Write down every second letter to find something to keep you warm.

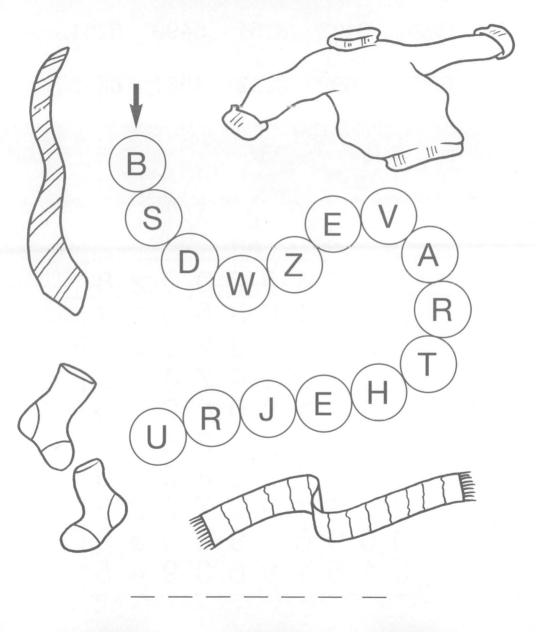

_ _ _ _ _ _ _

Secret numbers

Find the number sequences hidden in the grid.
Look up, down, across, and diagonally.

0028   0103   3151   5499   6251

0384   6092   2212   4581   8215

```
1 5 4 4 0 0 0 0 2 8
9 2 0 1 0 3 6 0 4 2
7 3 9 8 4 8 2 5 5 1
2 1 6 3 9 4 7 4 2 5
4 5 8 1 8 0 1 2 2 0
9 4 3 2 6 6 2 5 1 2
0 9 8 9 9 3 8 6 2 0
2 9 4 1 0 6 7 9 2 8
0 0 9 6 0 9 2 5 3 9
3 1 5 1 9 6 3 9 4 5
```

Mystery set

Cross out 4 vehicles, 4 sweet treats, and 4 birds in the selection below.
What connects the remaining words?

GOLF

TART

BICYCLE

FINCH

TRAIN

MUFFIN

EAGLE

SEAGULL

TENNIS

DONUT

CAR

OSTRICH

BUS

SQUASH

SPONGE

Sailing

Study this fleet of yachts heading out to sea and then answer the questions below.

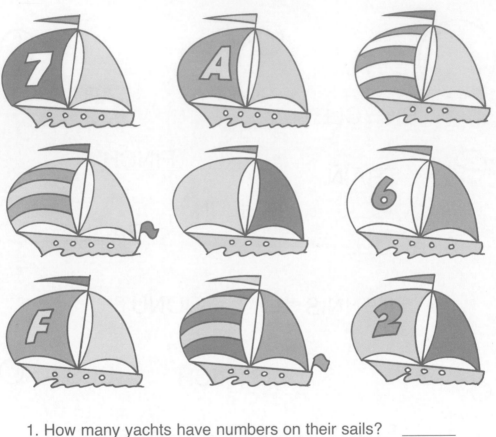

1. How many yachts have numbers on their sails? _____

2. How many yachts have two flags flying? _____

3. How many yachts have three portholes? _____

4. How many yachts have a striped sail? _____

5. How many yachts have letters on their sails? _____

Sports fans

Timmy, Kate, and David love to do sport. Follow the trails to find out which ones they like best!

Fast cat

Follow the start arrow and the compass clues
to find the fastest animal in the world!

5 squares West ___
2 squares North ___
2 squares West ___
2 squares North ___
4 squares East ___
2 squares North ___
4 squares West ___

___ ___ ___ ___ ___ ___ ___

H	W	Q	Q	A	T	O
V	Z	V	L	D	A	J
E	M	X	Y	T	U	X
G	X	K	A	T	P	F
E	W	H	L	R	X	B
J	K	I	K	L	D	R
G	E	C	Z	B	W	U

START ←

Count to 35

There are 5 pairs of numbers that add up to 35 in the grid.
Can you circle them?

2	30	5	15	7
8	4	25	10	3
23	12	11	6	8
4	10	3	27	8
6	21	14	6	9

Crunchy fruit

Break the code to find out what type of apple this is
before the worm eats it all!

‾‾ ‾‾ ‾‾ ‾‾ ‾‾ ‾‾   ‾‾ ‾‾ ‾‾ ‾‾ ‾‾
13 24 7 20 20 5   25 19 15 26 14

Dizzy digits

Fill in the grid so that each row, column, and mini-square contains a number from 1 to 4.

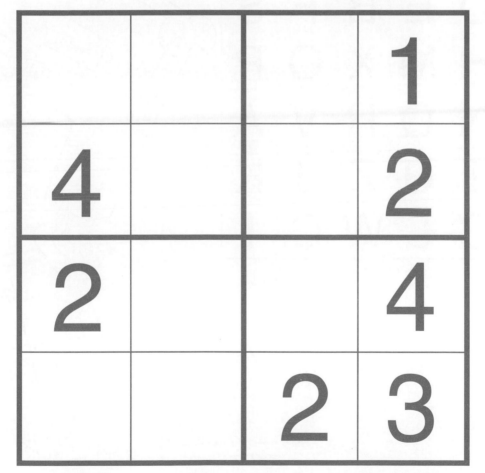

Letter pairs

In this grid, there are 5 pairs of letters that sit next to each other in the alphabet. Can you circle them?

D	E	B	F	S
H	M	X	O	P
N	Q	R	V	A
T	U	Z	J	K
G	L	W	C	I

Woof, woof

Follow the trail and write down every second letter to find a breed of dog.

_ _ _ _ _ _ _ _ _ _ _ _ _

I spy

Find the number sequences hidden in the grid.
Look up, down, across, and diagonally.

2027	3591	6802	5398	1001
6957	2840	3100	8853	4020

```
4 0 8 6 8 4 7 3 8 7
0 6 3 9 5 0 2 1 9 6
2 8 2 3 9 2 1 0 0 1
9 0 1 1 7 0 4 0 6 4
3 2 0 2 7 9 1 5 6 8
0 8 8 9 6 4 7 6 9 5
5 2 8 2 1 0 2 3 5 0
3 8 5 0 3 5 9 1 7 3
9 7 3 5 7 4 8 5 9 4
8 3 6 1 2 8 4 0 3 1
```

Treasure hunt

Cross out 4 snakes, 4 musical instruments, and 4 types of home in the selection below. What connects the remaining words?

BUNGALOW

DRUM

BOA

RUBY

COBRA

APARTMENT

HOUSE

VIOLIN

ANACONDA DIAMOND

VIPER

PIANO

CABIN

PEARL FLUTE

Ahoy

Study this pirate crew and answer the questions below.

1. How many pirates have a parrot on their shoulder? _____

2. How many pirates have a cutlass? _____

3. How many pirates have a pistol? _____

4. How many pirates have a hook? _____

5. How many pirates have a wooden leg? _____

Solar system

Which planets are these? Follow the star trails to find out!

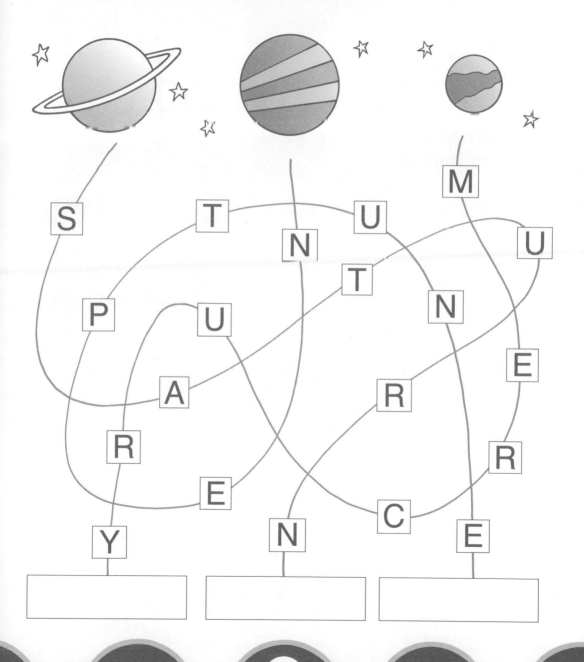

Mystery money

Follow the start arrow and the compass clues to find the name of a currency.

3 squares East   __

1 square North   __

4 squares East   __

3 squares North __

6 squares West __

2 squares North __

__ __ __ __ __ __

R	H	K	O	E	C	V
W	Q	Z	J	L	R	D
A	G	U	W	A	M	L
O	L	W	X	Z	Q	H
E	I	X	U	J	P	W
Q	Z	O	U	E	L	L
S	K	D	X	M	S	P

START →

Count to 40

There are 5 pairs of numbers that add up to 40 in the grid.
Can you circle them?

20	20	8	10	6
6	11	9	30	10
5	25	15	10	4
1	22	18	6	11
12	4	32	8	8

Woolly creature

Break the code to find out who has lost this sheep.

— — — — — —   — —   — — — —
18 15 26 26 18 11   8 21   22 11 11 22

Total numbers

Fill in the grid so that each row, column, and mini-square contains a number from 1 to 4.

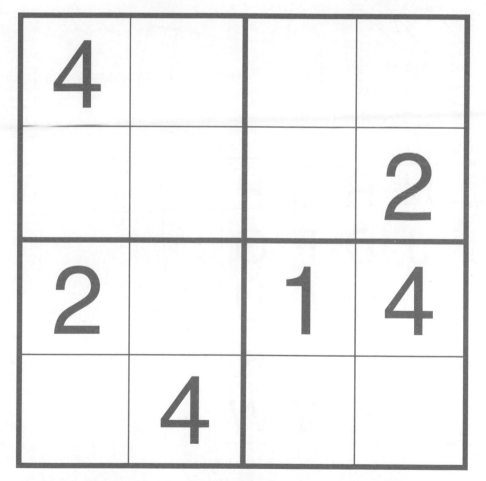

Hidden letters

In this grid, there are 5 pairs of letters that sit next to each other in the alphabet. Can you circle them?

L	N	R	S	P
I	J	D	F	G
A	T	M	C	U
O	Y	Z	B	K
X	H	E	V	W

Lizard king

Follow the trail and write down every second
letter to find the king of dinosaurs.

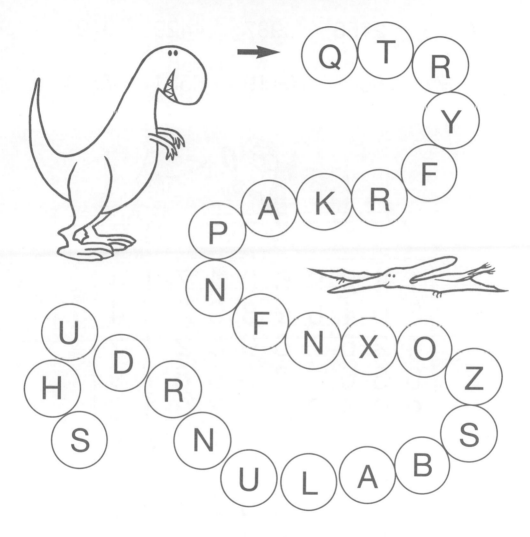

_ _ _ _ _ _ _ _ _ _ _ _

Break the code

Help Tom and Spot find the number sequences hidden in the grid.
Look up, down, across, and diagonally.

0109	2156	3987	4429	0101
2577	6543	0119	6531	7771

```
1 8 2 9 6 0 4 7 1 4
3 0 1 0 9 8 9 2 5 4
4 2 5 7 6 0 5 2 1 2
0 5 6 1 2 3 9 8 7 9
9 6 4 9 8 1 7 3 1 3
2 5 7 2 5 7 7 4 6 9
8 3 4 5 3 4 7 3 5 3
0 1 0 1 9 5 7 5 4 8
7 3 6 2 6 4 1 6 3 6
2 7 8 0 1 1 9 6 7 5
```

Busy bodies

Cross out 4 wild animals, 4 fruits, and 4 spices in the selection below.
What connects the remaining words?

MONKEY VANILLA PEAR

CINNAMON GIRAFFE

NUTMEG

APPLE ANT

BEE

ORANGE

GINGER

TIGER WASP

BANANA SNAKE

Knights of the round table

These knights are all ready for battle. Study them carefully then answer the questions below.

1. How many knights have a feather in their helmet? _____

2. How many knights have a striped shield? _____

3. How many knights are holding a lance? _____

4. How many knights have a sword? _____

5. How many knights have a flag? _____

Spot the dog

Woof! Follow the trails to spell out three types of dogs.
Write the answers in the boxes.

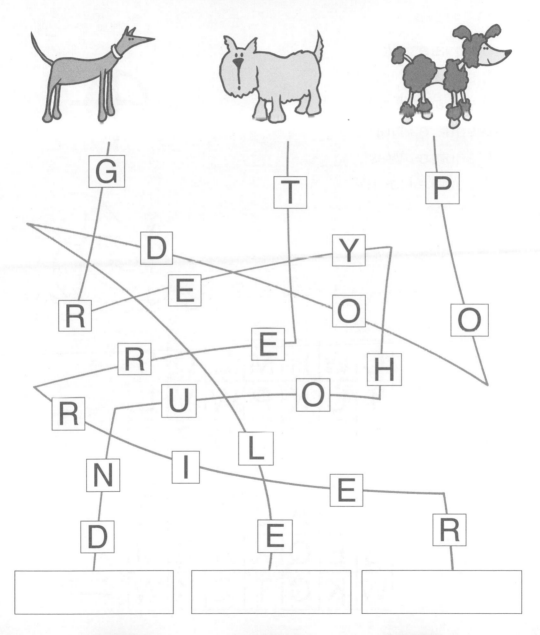

Smelly veg

Follow the start arrow and the compass clues to catch up with this stinky dude.

5 squares West ___
2 squares North ___
4 squares East ___
3 squares North ___
6 squares West ___
1 square North ___

N
W   E
S

__ __ __ __ __ __

C	W	H	M	L	D	S
I	U	K	P	W	V	L
G	J	T	L	Q	Z	I
Q	Z	H	Y	S	K	W
X	V	A	J	Q	I	R
S	E	Q	X	A	Z	M
W	K	G	T	Z	K	W

← START

Count to 45

There are 5 pairs of numbers that add up to 45 in the grid.
Can you circle them?

40	5	15	10	4
5	25	20	12	6
8	15	7	30	15
35	10	10	8	14
11	4	28	17	5

Sir what?

He's got his helmet on so you'll have to break the code
to identify this legendary knight.

___ ___ ___ ___ ___ ___ ___ ___

18   7   20   9   11   18   21   26

Mystery figures

Fill in the grid so that each row, column, and mini-square contains a number from 1 to 4.

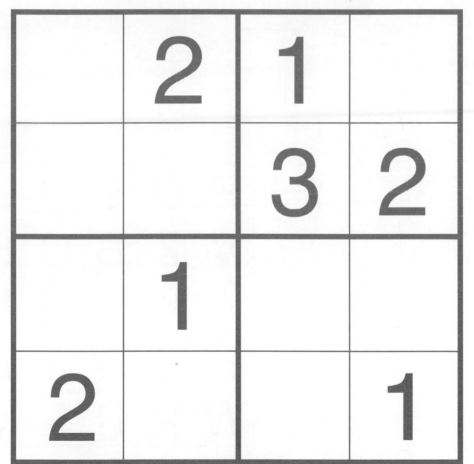

	2	1	
		3	2
	1		
2			1

Find the letters

In this grid, there are 5 pairs of letters that sit next to each other in the alphabet. Can you circle them?

P	Q	T	U	O
V	Z	B	G	H
A	K	I	S	N
F	C	D	J	E
W	X	R	L	M

Slippery game

Follow the trail and write down every second
letter to find a board game.

_ _ _ _ _ _ _ _ _ _

_ _ _ _ _ _

Number teasers

Find the number sequences hidden in the grid.
Look up, down, across, and diagonally.

0667	6969	4395	4350	5509
8210	0033	5449	2198	7815

```
5 4 4 9 6 0 4 7 1 4
3 0 5 0 9 7 8 1 5 8
4 2 5 7 6 0 5 2 1 2
0 5 0 6 6 7 9 8 2 9
9 6 9 9 8 8 7 3 1 3
5 5 7 2 5 2 7 4 9 9
9 3 4 5 3 1 7 3 8 3
3 1 4 3 5 0 7 5 4 8
4 3 6 2 6 0 0 3 3 6
2 7 6 9 6 9 9 6 7 5
```

Black and white?

Cross out 4 farm animals, 4 countries, and 4 fish in the selection below.
What connects the remaining words?

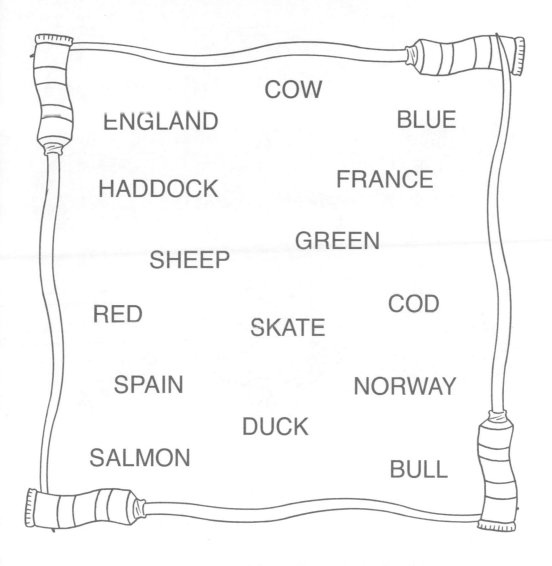

COW

ENGLAND

BLUE

HADDOCK

FRANCE

GREEN

SHEEP

RED

COD

SKATE

SPAIN

NORWAY

DUCK

SALMON

BULL

Down in the woods

Study this woodland carefully and answer the questions below.

1. How many trees have birds in them? _____

2. How many trees are losing their leaves? _____

3. How many trees have a hole in the trunk? _____

4. How many trees have apples? _____

5. How many trees have a squirrel in them? _____

Get dressed

Follow the trails to spell out three pieces of clothing.
Write the answers in the boxes.

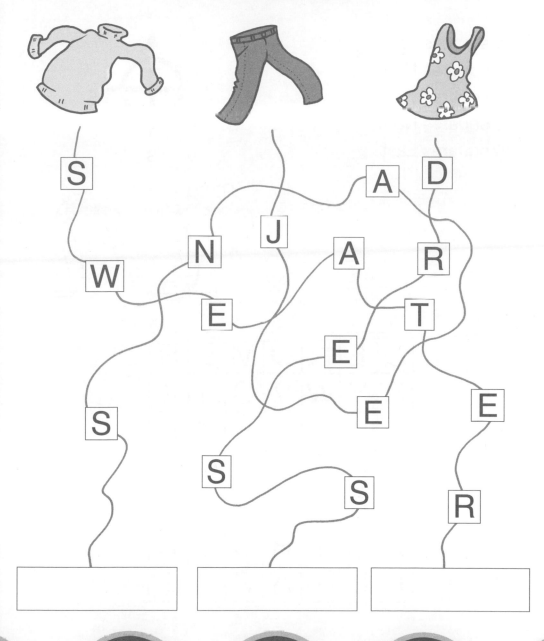

Slithery snake

This lurking snake has a nasty bite! Follow the start arrow and the compass clues to reveal what it is.

4 squares East ___
2 squares North ___
2 squares West ___
4 squares North ___
5 squares East ___

___ ___ ___ ___ ___

O	E	D	Q	M	L	R
S	Y	W	V	C	J	K
I	A	S	K	F	P	H
K	R	Y	D	K	O	Q
S	D	J	D	L	Y	B
W	G	Y	R	O	G	K
D	U	X	A	Z	Q	I

START →

Count to 50

There are 5 pairs of numbers that add up to 50 in the grid.
Can you circle them?

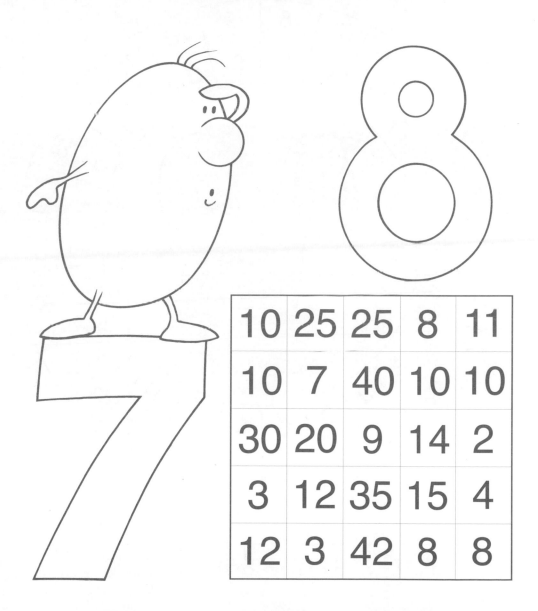

10	25	25	8	11
10	7	40	10	10
30	20	9	14	2
3	12	35	15	4
12	3	42	8	8

Horsey business

Break the code to find a handsome horse.

___ ___ ___ ___ ___   ___ ___ ___ ___ ___ ___
8 18 7   9 17   8 11 7   1 26 5

Square the numbers

Fill in the grid so that each row, column, and mini-square contains a number from 1 to 4.

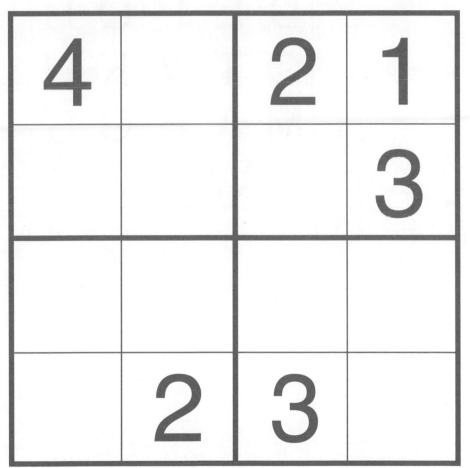

Triple letters

In this grid, there are 4 sets of 3 letters that sit next to each other in the alphabet. Can you circle them?

G	H	I	L	N
D	E	P	Q	R
O	T	Y	K	U
M	A	B	C	S
V	W	X	F	J

Tutti frutti

Follow the trail and write down every second letter to find a juicy fruit.

_ _ _ _ _ _ _ _ _ _ _ _

Math quiz

Help Ben and Rover find the number sequences hidden in the grid.
Look up, down, across, and diagonally.

1469   4680   2145   4678   8800

0015   6231   5612   4478   9321

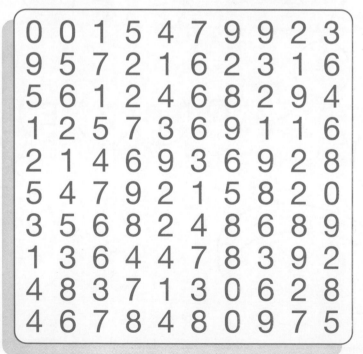

0	0	1	5	4	7	9	9	2	3
9	5	7	2	1	6	2	3	1	6
5	6	1	2	4	6	8	2	9	4
1	2	5	7	3	6	9	1	1	6
2	1	4	6	9	3	6	9	2	8
5	4	7	9	2	1	5	8	2	0
3	5	6	8	2	4	8	6	8	9
1	3	6	4	4	7	8	3	9	2
4	8	3	7	1	3	0	6	2	8
4	6	7	8	4	8	0	9	7	5

Healthy mix

Cross out 4 types of dog, 4 continents, and 4 reptiles in the selection below. What connects the remaining words?

RATTLESNAKE

BOXER

PYTHON

TERRIER

AMERICA

AFRICA

LEEKS

LIZARD

SPANIEL

ONIONS

TORTOISE

EUROPE

CARROTS

GREYHOUND

ASIA

At the ballet

These dancers are all practicing for a big show. Study them carefully and then answer the questions below.

1. How many dancers have ponytails? _____

2. How many dancers are standing on tip toe? _____

3. How many dancers have their hands above their heads? _____

4. How many dancers have dark ballet shoes? _____

5. How many dancers are wearing leggings? _____

Thirsty work!

Follow the trails to spell out three delicious drinks.
Write the answers in the boxes.

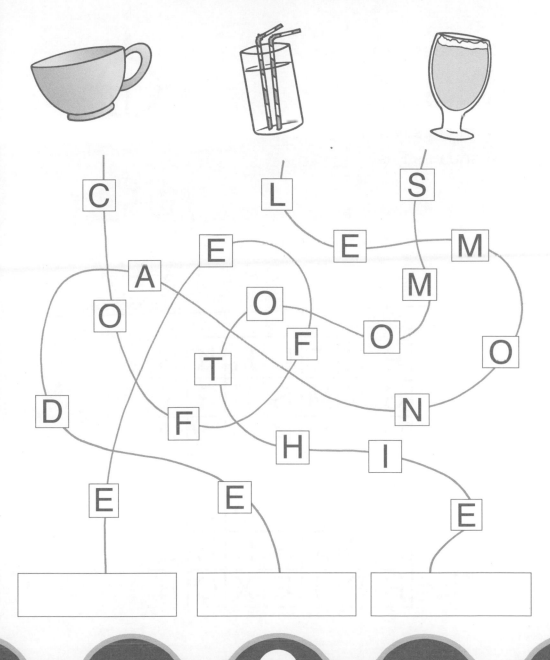

Who's this?

Follow the start arrow and the compass clues to reveal this boy's name.

3 squares East   J

2 squares North   A

2 squares West   M

4 squares North   E

6 squares East   S

J A M E S

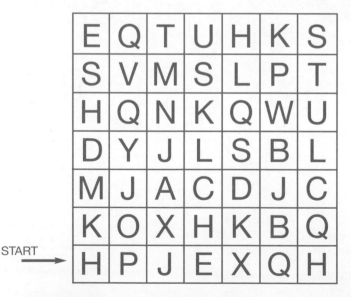

E	Q	T	U	H	K	S
S	V	M	S	L	P	T
H	Q	N	K	Q	W	U
D	Y	J	L	S	B	L
M	J	A	C	D	J	C
K	O	X	H	K	B	Q
H	P	J	E	X	Q	H

START →

Count to 55

There are 5 pairs of numbers that add up to 55 in the grid.
Can you circle them?

50	5	20	8	11
12	5	40	15	5
6	20	30	25	5
35	20	8	15	15
7	15	5	37	18

Month mix-up

This calendar has got all muddled!
Break the code to find out which month it is.

$\overline{}$ $\overline{}$ $\overline{}$ $\overline{}$ $\overline{}$ $\overline{}$ $\overline{}$

21   9   26   21   8   11   24

Square riddles

Fill in the grid so that each row, column, and mini-square contains a number from 1 to 4.

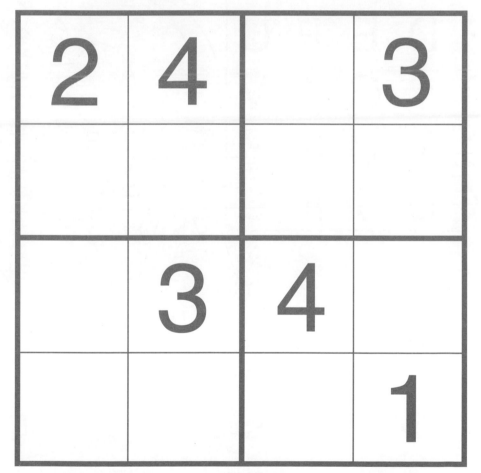

2	4		3
	3	4	
			1

Letter puzzle

In this grid, there are 4 sets of 3 letters that sit next to each other in the alphabet. Can you circle them?

Q	M	N	O	W
P	D	E	F	C
R	I	G	A	V
S	T	U	H	Y
X	B	J	K	L

Snap, snap!

Which reptile is on the prowl? Follow the trail and write down every second letter to find out.

‒ ‒ ‒ ‒ ‒ ‒ ‒ ‒

Nutty numbers

Find the number sequences hidden in the grid.
Look up, down, across, and diagonally.

3456   8742   0001   4379   2947

0213   8340   5878   4446   9034

```
1 3 4 5 6 1 1 0 1 7
4 8 5 4 5 3 4 2 4 4
7 9 0 3 4 5 7 1 7 8
4 2 8 2 8 7 9 3 3 7
4 3 7 9 3 9 7 6 5 4
4 5 3 4 5 2 3 9 8 2
6 1 9 7 8 5 6 3 5 8
9 9 3 7 8 8 3 4 0 4
4 2 2 3 3 7 4 6 8 3
0 0 0 1 6 8 2 1 2 9
```

Money-go-round

Cross out 4 items of clothing, 4 types of pet, and 4 types of bike in the selection below. What connects the remaining words?

TANDEM

CAT

GLOVE

COAT

RACING

EURO

HAT

DOLLAR

HAMSTER

DOG

SHIRT

BMX

POUND

MOUNTAIN

BUDGIE

Flower pots

These flowers are lined up to be judged in a flower show.
Study them carefully and answer the questions below.

1. How many flowers have five petals? _____

2. How many flowerpots have stripes? _____

3. How many flowerpots have zig zags? _____

4. How many flowers have four petals? _____

5. How many flowerpots have two flowers? _____

Fruit bowl

Follow the trails to spell out three types of fruit.
Write the answers in the boxes.

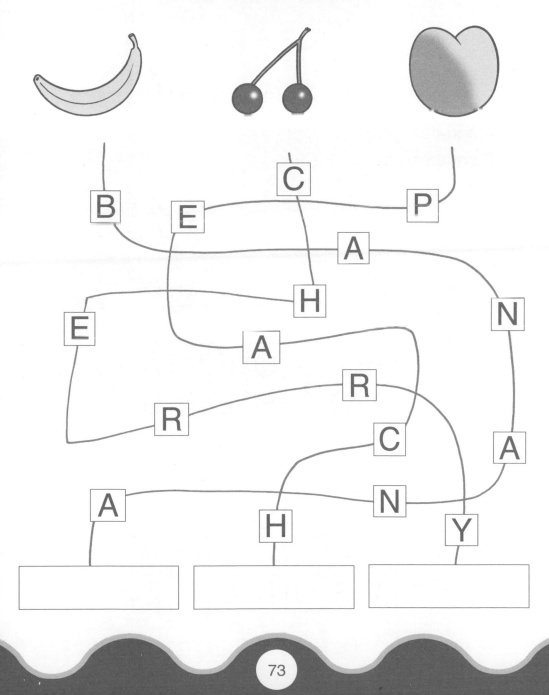

Take out

Follow the start arrow and the compass clues to find out
what type of fast food the man is delivering.

6 squares East ___
2 squares North ___
4 squares West ___
4 squares North ___
5 squares East ___

N

W ⊕ E

S

___ ___ ___ ___ ___

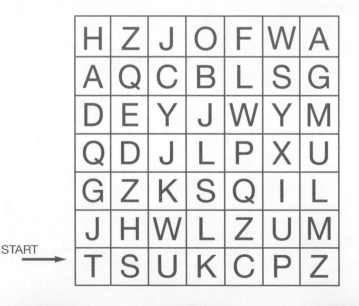

H	Z	J	O	F	W	A
A	Q	C	B	L	S	G
D	E	Y	J	W	Y	M
Q	D	J	L	P	X	U
G	Z	K	S	Q	I	L
J	H	W	L	Z	U	M
T	S	U	K	C	P	Z

START →

74

Count to 60

There are 5 pairs of numbers that add up to 60 in the grid.
Can you circle them?

Where in America?

Break the code to find one of the 50 states.

9	7	18	15	12	21	24	20	15	7

Funky figures

Fill in the grid so that each row, column, and mini-square contains a number from 1 to 4.

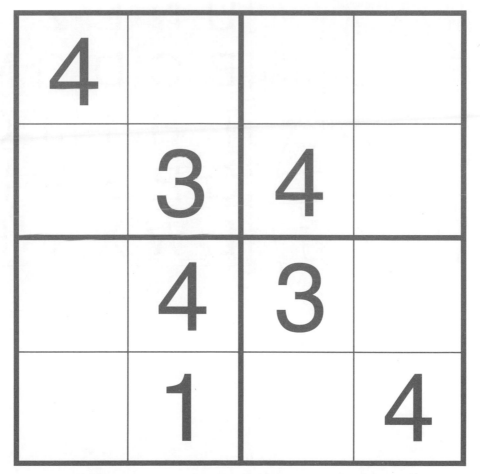

Alphabetical

In this grid, there are 4 sets of 3 letters that sit next to each other in the alphabet. Can you circle them?

U	N	P	Z	T
B	C	D	G	M
L	H	I	J	O
Q	R	S	V	K
E	W	X	Y	F

All shook up!

Follow the trail and write down every second letter to find a type of drink.

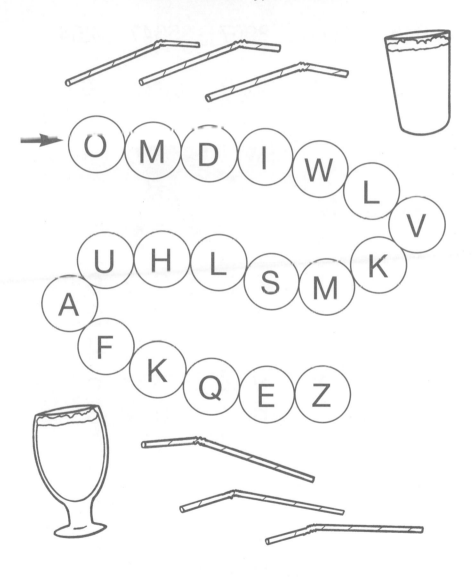

_ _ _ _ _ _ _ _ _

Number crunching

Find the number sequences hidden in the grid.
Look up, down, across, and diagonally.

5645   2314   8967   5347   2541

8679   3691   4589   2634   8560

5 6 4 5 1 3 5 2 7 9
3 9 6 3 1 7 5 3 3 2
4 1 4 6 9 8 2 1 9 2
7 3 5 7 9 2 5 4 1 6
5 8 9 3 6 7 4 9 2 8
2 6 3 4 9 7 3 1 4 5
3 7 5 9 3 6 9 1 3 6
6 9 9 7 2 5 9 1 2 0
9 7 4 4 5 8 9 2 6 9
2 4 6 8 3 5 8 9 6 7

Woody walk

Cross out 4 types of weather, 4 cities, and 4 types of tool in the selection below. What connects the remaining words?

SUNSHINE

BEECH

DRILL

SNOW

LONDON

WIND

NEW YORK

AX

HAMMER

TOKYO

SCREWDRIVER

PINE

OAK

MOSCOW

RAIN

Something fishy

Study the fish in the aquarium and answer the questions below.

1. How many fish are striped? _____

2. How many fish have spots? _____

3. How many fish are long and thin? _____

4. How many fish are blowing bubbles? _____

5. How many fish have big tails? _____

What's the weather?

Follow the trails to spell out three types of weather.
Write the answers in the boxes.

Pick a color

Follow the start arrow and the compass clues to find
the frog's favorite color.

3 squares East   ___
2 squares North ___
1 square West   ___
4 squares North ___
5 squares East   ___

___ ___ ___ ___ ___

Q	E	T	A	G	K	N
S	W	H	E	M	W	P
G	D	K	P	Z	Q	H
N	F	O	K	K	R	L
K	E	R	H	C	N	U
P	V	A	Q	W	S	K
M	N	G	Z	A	I	S

START →

Count to 65

There are 5 pairs of numbers that add up to 65 in the grid.
Can you circle them?

50	15	15	30	8
11	10	5	55	10
30	9	45	20	20
6	35	30	20	10
3	9	10	40	25

Over the sea

Break the code to find a type of noisy seabird.

— — — — — — —
25 11 7 13 1 18 18

Number grids

Fill in the grid so that each row, column, and mini-square contains a number from 1 to 4.

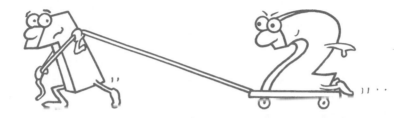

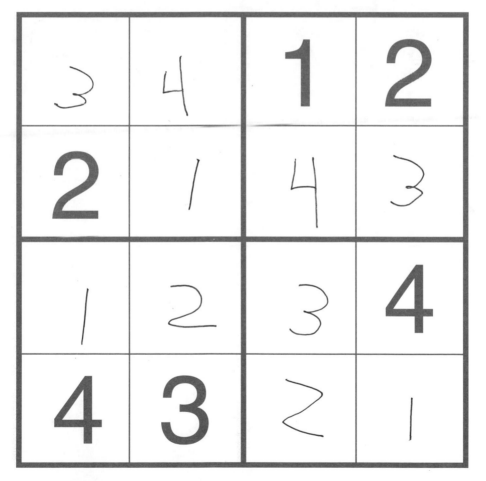

3	4	1	2
2	1	4	3
1	2	3	4
4	3	2	1

Secret letters

In this grid, there are 4 sets of 3 letters that sit next to each other in the alphabet. Can you circle them?

H	C	E	F	G
W	B	S	X	J
T	U	V	R	D
A	K	L	M	I
Y	Q	N	O	P

Going places

Follow the trail and write down every
second letter to find a type of transport.

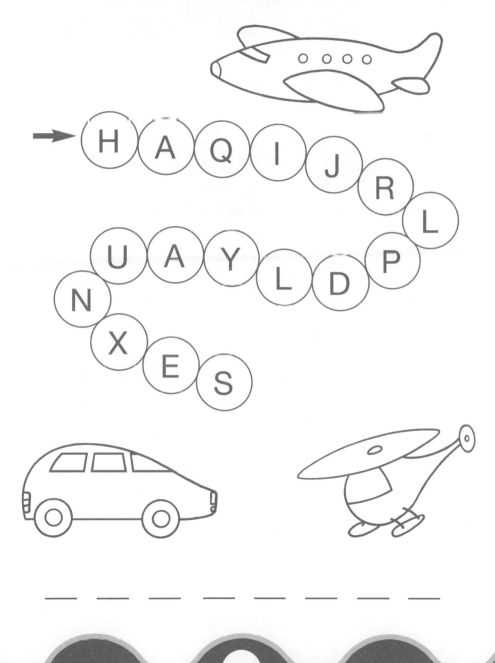

_ _ _ _ _ _ _ _

Find the numbers

Find the number sequences hidden in the grid.
Look up, down, across, and diagonally.

5768   0034   6471   5634   2323

9123   3595   5231   7562   0341

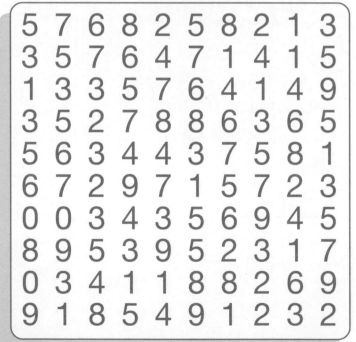

5	7	6	8	2	5	8	2	1	3
3	5	7	6	4	7	1	4	1	5
1	3	3	5	7	6	4	1	4	9
3	5	2	7	8	8	6	3	6	5
5	6	3	4	4	3	7	5	8	1
6	7	2	9	7	1	5	7	2	3
0	0	3	4	3	5	6	9	4	5
8	9	5	3	9	5	2	3	1	7
0	3	4	1	1	8	8	2	6	9
9	1	8	5	4	9	1	2	3	2

Yummy snacks

Cross out 4 months of the year, 4 swimming strokes, and 4 types of music in the selection below. What connects the remaining words?

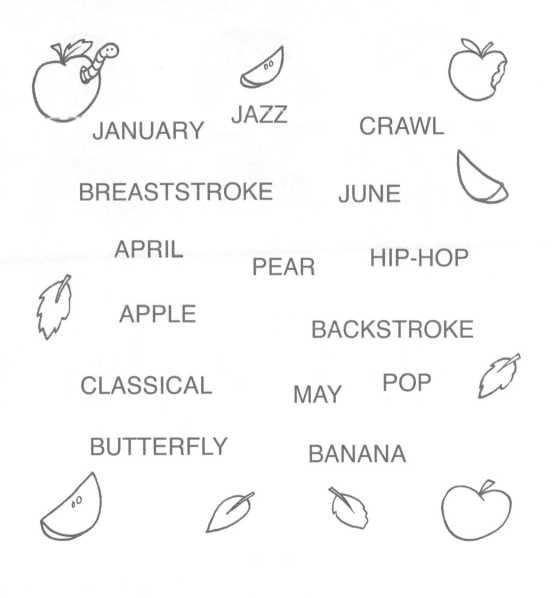

JANUARY JAZZ CRAWL

BREASTSTROKE JUNE

APRIL

PEAR HIP-HOP

APPLE

BACKSTROKE

CLASSICAL MAY POP

BUTTERFLY BANANA

Funny faces

This class is ready for their school picture. Look at them closely and answer the questions below.

1. How many faces are happy? _____

2. How many faces are sad? _____

3. How many faces have tongues sticking out? _____

4. How many faces are winking? _____

5. How many faces are asleep? _____

Where am I from?

Nick, Eva, and Harry are all from different countries.
Follow the trails to find out which ones.

Hard cheese

This mouse has managed to grab a nice, big lump of cheese. Follow the start arrow and the compass clues to find out what type it is.

5 squares East ___
1 square North ___
4 squares West ___
2 squares North ___
6 squares East ___
3 squares North ___
6 squares West ___

___ ___ ___ ___ ___ ___ ___

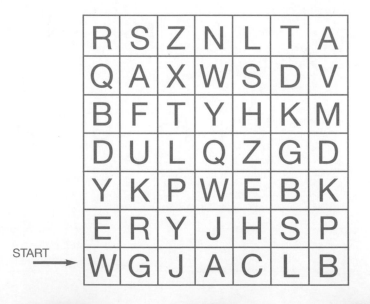

R	S	Z	N	L	T	A
Q	A	X	W	S	D	V
B	F	T	Y	H	K	M
D	U	L	Q	Z	G	D
Y	K	P	W	E	B	K
E	R	Y	J	H	S	P
W	G	J	A	C	L	B

START →

Count to 70

There are 5 pairs of numbers that add up to 70 in the grid.
Can you circle them?

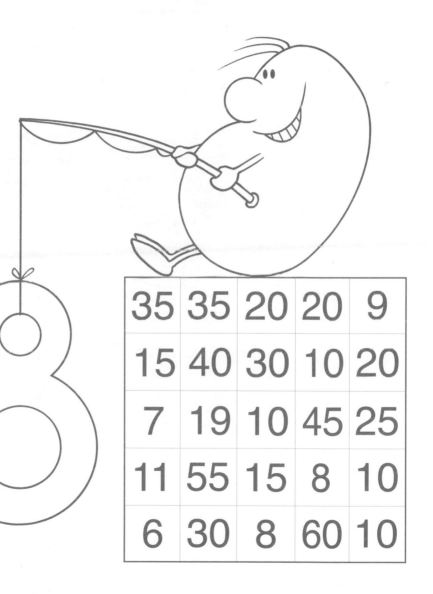

35	35	20	20	9
15	40	30	10	20
7	19	10	45	25
11	55	15	8	10
6	30	8	60	10

At the bakers

Break the code to find what kind of bread the
baker has made this morning.

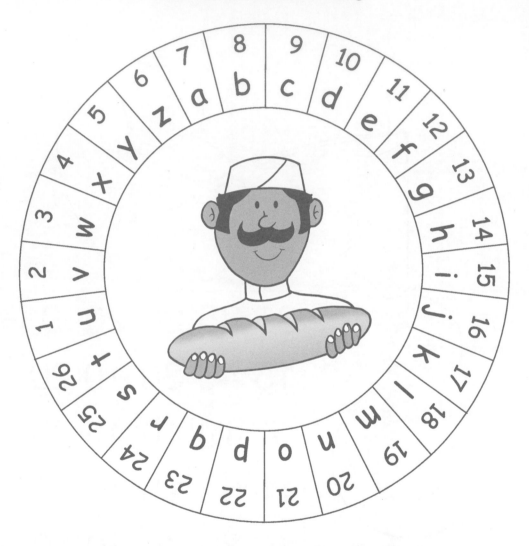

—   —   —   —   —   —   —   —
8   7   13   1   11   26   26   11

Tricky numbers

Fill in the grid so that each row, column, and mini-square contains a number from 1 to 4.

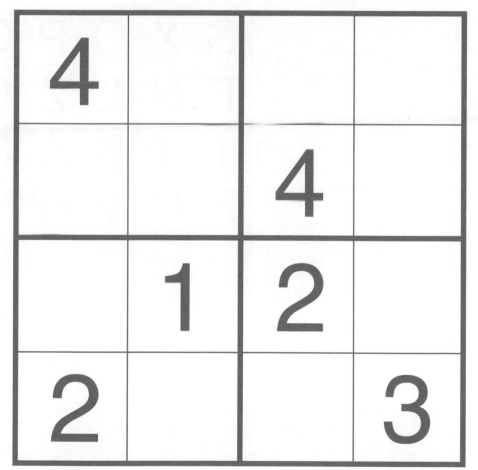

Chain letters

In this grid, there are 4 sets of 3 letters that sit next to each other in the alphabet. Can you circle them?

Y	C	D	E	T
G	X	O	P	Q
F	N	L	Z	H
I	J	K	A	S
B	U	V	W	M

In space

Follow the trail and write down every second letter to find a distant giant planet.

_ _ _ _ _ _ _ _

Silly sums

Find the number sequences hidden in the grid.
Look up, down, across, and diagonally.

4621	7834	0034	6112	9900
2121	5667	7834	0032	5645

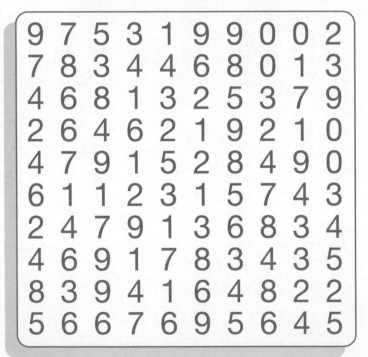

```
9 7 5 3 1 9 9 0 0 2
7 8 3 4 4 6 8 0 1 3
4 6 8 1 3 2 5 3 7 9
2 6 4 6 2 1 9 2 1 0
4 7 9 1 5 2 8 4 9 0
6 1 1 2 3 1 5 7 4 3
2 4 7 9 1 3 6 8 3 4
4 6 9 1 7 8 3 4 3 5
8 3 9 4 1 6 4 8 2 2
5 6 6 7 6 9 5 6 4 5
```

What's a foot?

Cross out 4 baby animals, 4 things to do with Christmas, and 4 circus acts in the selection below. What connects the remaining words?

SHOE

ACROBAT

LAMB   CLOWN

KITTEN

FOAL

MISTLETOE   PRESENT

FIRE-EATER   BOOT

SANTA

SLEIGH   JUGGLER

PUPPY

SNEAKER

Cat show

These pretty kitties are all lined up for judging. Look at them carefully and answer the questions below.

1. How many cats have stripes? _____

2. How many cats have two black paws? _____

3. How many cats have collars? _____

4. How many cats have no whiskers? _____

5. How many cats have four white paws? _____

Rainbow colors

Follow the trails to spell out three colors of the rainbow.
Write the answers in the boxes.

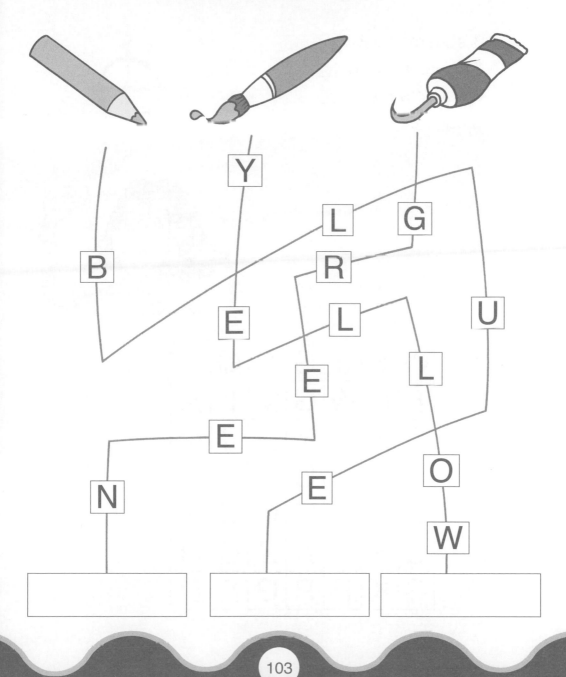

Shiny stone

Follow the start arrow and the compass clues to find what Tina's birthstone is.

4 squares East ___
3 squares North ___
3 squares East ___
3 squares North ___

__ __ __ __

W	F	J	G	E	Q	Y
F	H	W	G	M	L	A
D	X	R	Y	H	J	I
S	R	W	U	M	A	B
X	K	A	T	O	X	E
G	S	R	A	Z	Q	H
G	K	P	R	G	S	D

START →

Count to 80

There are 5 pairs of numbers that add up to 80 in the grid.
Can you circle them?

40	40	20	15	7
20	5	70	10	20
10	60	20	20	10
10	20	50	30	9
65	15	25	15	10

Pussy cat

Break the code to find a type of fluffy cat.

| 22 | 11 | 24 | 25 | 15 | 7 | 20 |

Number fun

Fill in the grid so that each row, column, and mini-square contains a number from 1 to 4.

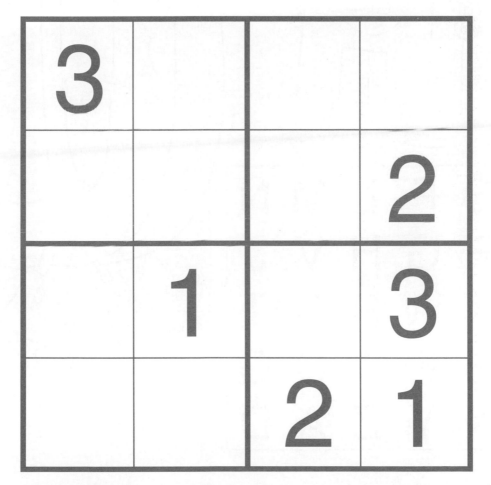

Letter grid

In this grid, there are 4 sets of 3 letters that sit next to each other in the alphabet. Can you circle them?

O	P	L	M	N
F	G	H	V	J
K	W	R	S	T
B	E	I	C	Q
X	Y	Z	A	D

Giant of the sea

Follow the trail and write down every second letter to find a giant sea creature.

— — — — — — — — —

Crack the code

Find the number sequences hidden in the grid.
Look up, down, across, and diagonally.

6678	9993	3535	2128	7788
1000	9080	2345	7569	1621

6	6	7	8	1	9	9	0	0	9
7	8	3	4	4	6	0	0	1	9
4	6	8	1	9	2	8	3	7	9
2	6	4	1	0	0	0	2	1	3
4	7	9	1	5	2	8	4	9	0
6	5	3	5	3	5	5	7	4	3
2	6	7	9	1	2	3	4	5	4
1	9	9	1	7	8	3	4	3	5
2	3	9	4	1	7	7	8	8	2
8	6	6	1	6	2	1	6	4	5

Tasty treat

Cross out 4 shellfish, 4 types of transport, and 4 games in the selection below. What connects the remaining words?

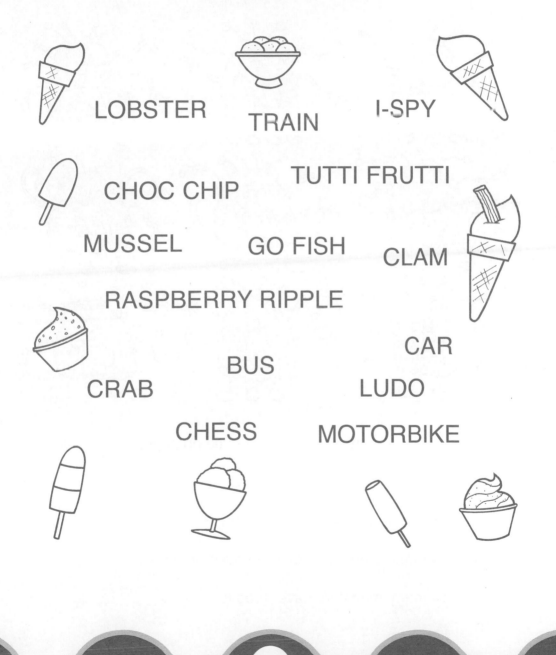

LOBSTER TRAIN I-SPY

CHOC CHIP TUTTI FRUTTI

MUSSEL GO FISH CLAM

RASPBERRY RIPPLE

CAR

BUS

CRAB LUDO

CHESS MOTORBIKE

Monster parade

These monsters are dancing at a party. Study them carefully
and answer the questions below.

1. How many monsters have four eyes on stalks? _____

2. How many monsters have four arms? _____

3. How many monsters have six arms? _____

4. How many monsters have five eyes on stalks? _____

5. How many monsters have three legs? _____

Bird bonanza

Follow the trails to spell out which birds are visiting the park today.
Write the answers in the boxes.

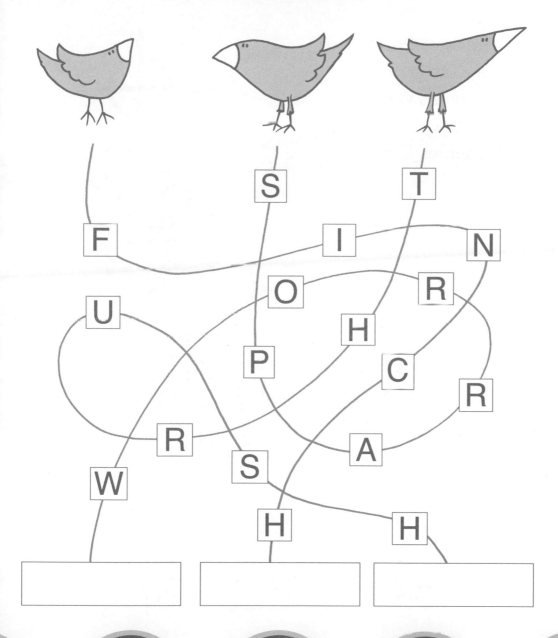

Sweet stuff

Follow the start arrow and the compass clues
to find out what Boris bee likes to eat.

4 squares East   ___
1 square North   ___
3 squares West   ___
5 squares North ___
6 squares East   ___

__ __ __ __ __

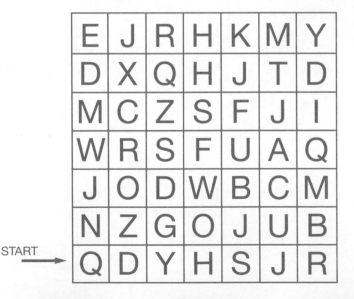

E	J	R	H	K	M	Y
D	X	Q	H	J	T	D
M	C	Z	S	F	J	I
W	R	S	F	U	A	Q
J	O	D	W	B	C	M
N	Z	G	O	J	U	B
Q	D	Y	H	S	J	R

START →

Count to 90

There are 5 pairs of numbers that add up to 90 in the grid.
Can you circle them?

8	20	45	45	20
5	80	10	15	9
30	8	10	60	30
50	40	30	15	9
20	10	65	25	20

On your head

Break the code to find a type of tall hairstyle from the 1960s.

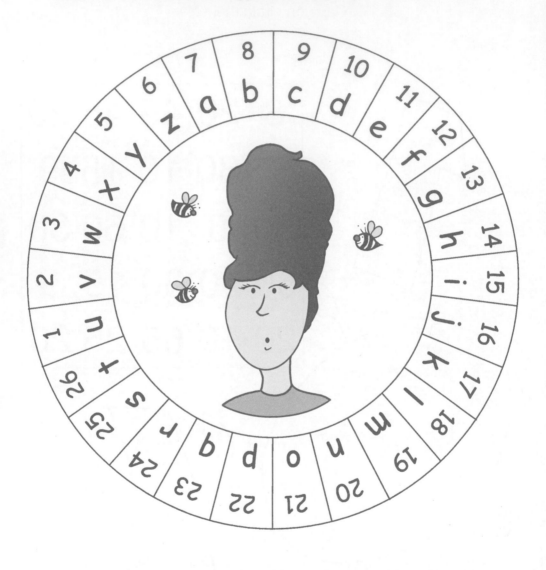

$\underline{\quad}$ $\underline{\quad}$ $\underline{\quad}$ $\underline{\quad}$ $\underline{\quad}$ $\underline{\quad}$ $\underline{\quad}$
  8   11   11   14   15   2   11

Number squares

Fill in the grid so that each row, column, and mini-square contains a number from 1 to 4.

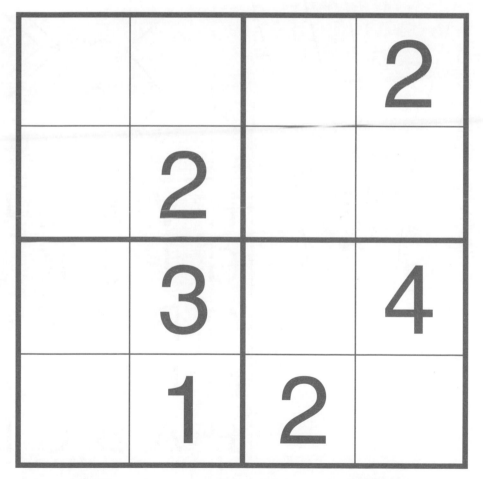

Letter square

In this grid, there are 3 sets of 4 letters that sit next to each other in the alphabet. Can you circle them?

E	V	X	Z	U
G	I	J	K	L
Q	R	S	T	O
M	F	W	Y	N
P	A	B	C	D

Hot wheels

Follow the trail and write down every second letter to find a type of car.

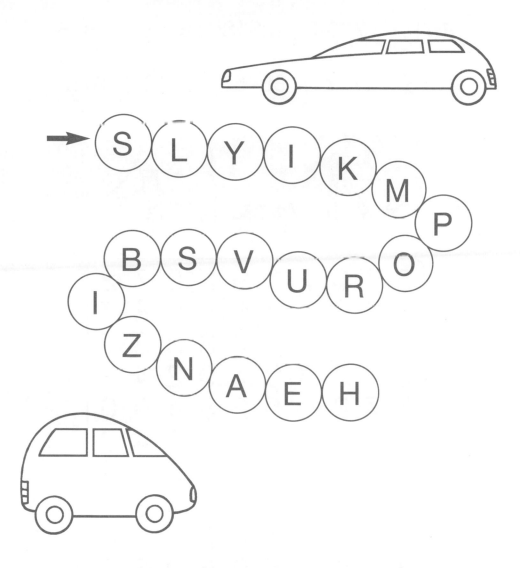

– – – – – – – – – –

What number?

Find the number sequences hidden in the grid.
Look up, down, across, and diagonally.

4645	7834	2518	5739	9898
1323	2777	3545	2310	6767

```
6 7 6 7 1 9 9 0 7 2
7 8 3 4 4 6 4 0 8 7
4 6 4 5 3 2 8 3 3 7
2 1 7 6 2 1 9 2 4 7
5 7 3 9 5 2 8 4 9 0
6 1 1 2 1 3 2 3 4 3
2 4 7 9 1 1 6 8 5 4
3 5 4 5 7 0 3 4 3 5
8 3 9 4 1 6 2 5 1 8
9 8 9 8 6 9 5 0 6 2
```

Funny felines

Cross out 4 flowers, 4 types of boat, and 4 fast foods in the selection below. What connects the remaining words?

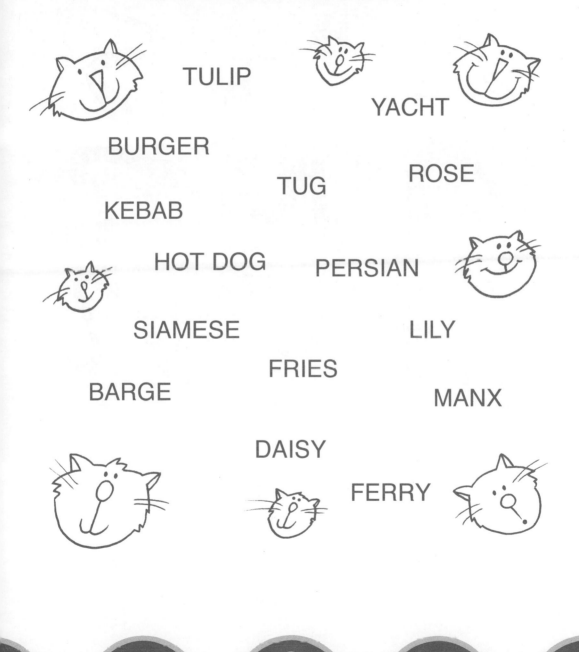

TULIP

YACHT

BURGER

ROSE

TUG

KEBAB

HOT DOG

PERSIAN

SIAMESE

LILY

FRIES

BARGE

MANX

DAISY

FERRY

Wriggly reptiles

These snakes have come out to bask in the sun. Look at them closely and answer the questions below.

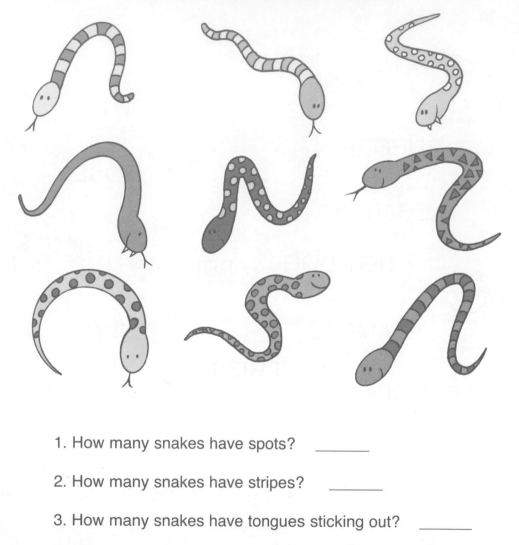

1. How many snakes have spots? _____

2. How many snakes have stripes? _____

3. How many snakes have tongues sticking out? _____

4. How many snakes have triangles? _____

5. How many snakes have fangs? _____

Wild cats

Follow the trails to spell out three types of fearsome felines.
Write the answers in the boxes.

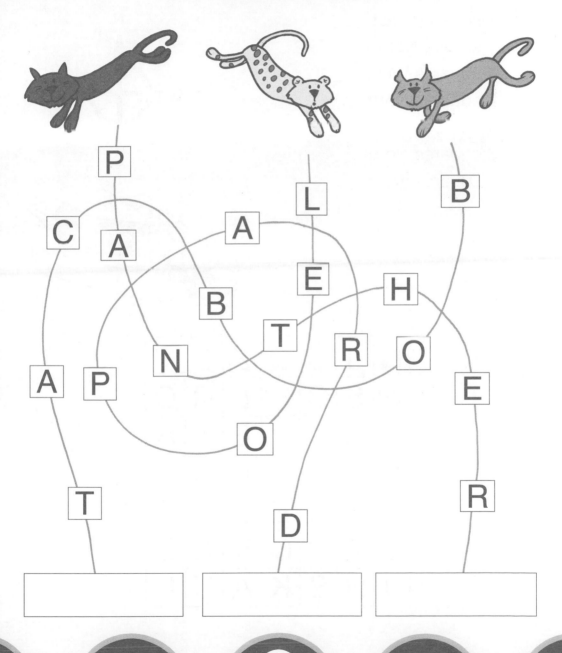

Little waiter

Follow the start arrow and the compass clues to find a type of bird.

7 squares East ___
1 square North ___
4 squares West ___
2 squares North ___
4 squares East ___
3 squares North ___
6 squares West ___

__ __ __ __ __ __ __

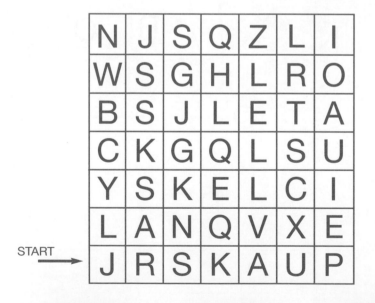

N	J	S	Q	Z	L	I
W	S	G	H	L	R	O
B	S	J	L	E	T	A
C	K	G	Q	L	S	U
Y	S	K	E	L	C	I
L	A	N	Q	V	X	E
J	R	S	K	A	U	P

START →

Count to 100

There are 5 pairs of numbers that add up to 100 in the grid.
Can you circle them?

20	50	50	15	18
5	16	30	60	40
9	80	20	30	15
70	30	50	10	9
8	40	5	90	10

Hear the beat

What kind of music does George like to play? Break the code to find out.

24 21 9 17   7 20 10   24 21 18 18

Four figures

Fill in the grid so that each row, column, and mini-square contains a number from 1 to 4.

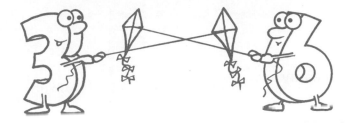

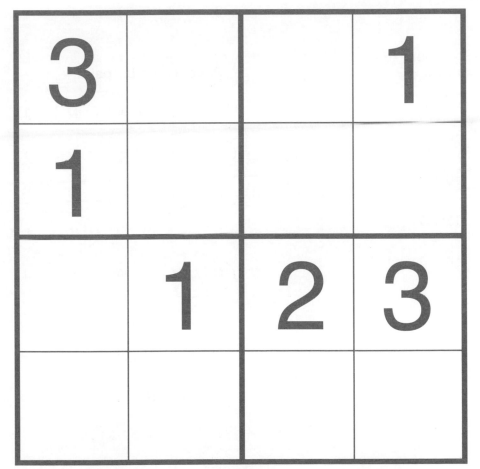

Answers

Page 3 – Find the fish

HERRING

Page 4 – Natural beauty

RAINBOW

Page 5 – Count to 20

19 + 1

16 + 4

10 + 10

15 + 5

14 + 6

Page 6 – Home sweet home

BUNGALOW

Page 7 – Number count

4	1	3	2
2	3	1	4
1	2	4	3
3	4	2	1

Page 8 – Letter pairs

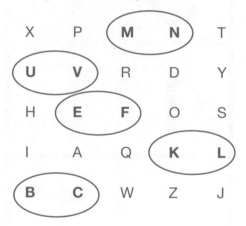

X	P	M	N	T
U	V	R	D	Y
H	E	F	O	S
I	A	Q	K	L
B	C	W	Z	J

Page 9 – Yummy cake

BROWNIES

Answers

Page 10 – Number magic

4　4　0　1

7	3	9	8	0	5	1
	1			2	4	2
	7			0	2	0
9	2			3	6	2
0		9	9	8	0	
2						
0	0	9	5			
			6	3	9	4

Page 11 – What's left?

They are all girl's names

KATY　　KELLY　　RACHEL

Page 12 – In the crowd

1. 1
2. 2
3. 2
4. 2
5. 3

Page 13 – Destinations

NEW YORK

LONDON

BERLIN

Page 14 – In the jungle

PARROT

Page 15 – Count to 30

15 + 15

10 + 20

18 + 12

29 + 1

14 + 16

Page 16 – What's my name?

NATHAN

SOPHIE

WILLIAM

Page 17 – Sum it up

4	2	1	3
1	3	2	4
3	1	4	2
2	4	3	1

Answers

Page 18 – Perfect pairs

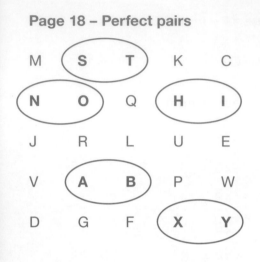

M (S T) K C
(N O) Q (H I)
J R L U E
V (A B) P W
D G F (X Y)

Page 19 – Wrap up warm

SWEATER

Page 20 – Secret numbers

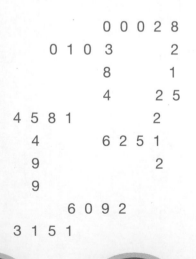

```
            0  0  0  2  8
     0  1  0  3        2
            8           1
            4        2  5
4  5  8  1           2
   4        6  2  5  1
   9                 2
   9
      6  0  9  2
3  1  5  1
```

Page 21 – Mystery set

They are all ball games

GOLF   TENNIS   SQUASH

Page 22 – Sailing

1. 3
2. 2
3. 3
4. 3
5. 2

Page 23 – Spots fans

SOCCER

TENNIS

SWIMMING

Page 24 – Fast cat

CHEETAH

Answers

Page 25 – Count to 35

30 + 5

15 + 10

23 + 15

27 + 8

21 + 14

Page 26 – Crunchy fruit

GRANNY SMITH

Page 27 – Dizzy digits

3	2	4	1
4	1	3	2
2	3	1	4
1	4	2	3

Page 28 – Letter pairs

(D	E)	B	F	S
H	M	X	(O	P)
N	(Q	R)	V	A
(T	U)	Z	(J	K)
G	L	W	C	I

Page 29 – Woof woof

GREYHOUND

Page 30 – I spy

```
            4   3
    6         0   1
    8         2 1 0 0 1
    0           0   0
      2 0 2 7           6
          8               9
    5   8                 5
    3   5     3 5 9 1 7
    9   3
    8         2 8 4 0
```

Answers

Page 31 – Treasure hunt

They are all gems

RUBY   PEARL   DIAMOND

Page 32 – Ahoy

1. 3
2. 4
3. 5
4. 2
5. 3

Page 33 – Solar system

SATURN

NEPTUNE

MERCURY

Page 34 – Mystery money

DOLLAR

Page 35 – Count to 40

20 + 20
30 + 10
25 + 15
22 + 18
32 + 8

Page 36 – Woolly creature

LITTLE BO PEEP

Page 37 – Total numbers

4	2	3	1
3	1	4	2
2	3	1	4
1	4	2	3

Page 38 – Hidden letters

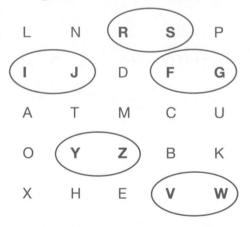

Page 39 – Lizard king

TYRANNOSAURUS

Answers

Page 40 – Break the code

```
    2                 4
0 1 0 9               4
    5                 2
    6       3 9 8 7 9
6
5     2 5 / /   6
3               7   5
0 1 0 1         7   4
                1   3
    0 1 1 9
```

Page 41 – Busy bodies

They are all insects

WASP   BEE   ANT

Page 42 – Knights of the round table

1. 4
2. 2
3. 1
4. 5
5. 2

Page 43 – Spot the dog

GREYHOUND

TERRIER

POODLE

Page 44 – Smelly veg

GARLIC

Page 45 – Count to 45

40 + 4

25 + 20

30 + 15

35 + 10

28 + 17

Page 46 – Sir what?

LANCELOT

Answers

Page 47 – Mystery figures

3	2	1	4
1	4	3	2
4	1	2	3
2	3	4	1

Page 48 – Find the letters

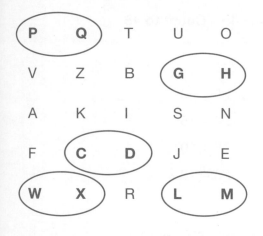

Page 49 – Slippery game

CHUTES AND LADDERS

Page 50 – Number teasers

```
5 4 4 9
    5       7 8 1 5
    5
    0 6 6 7       2
    9       8       1
5           2       9
9           1       8
3   4 3 5 0
4           0 0 3 3
    6 9 6 9
```

Page 51 – Not just black and white

They are all colors

BLUE   GREEN   RED

Page 52 – Down in the woods

1. 3
2. 2
3. 1
4. 4
5. 2

Answers

Page 53 – Get dressed

SWEATER

JEANS

DRESS

Page 54 – Slithery snake

ADDER

Page 55 – Count to 50

25 + 25

40 + 10

30 + 20

35 + 15

42 + 8

Page 56 – Horsey business

BLACK BEAUTY

Page 57 – Square the numbers

4   3   2   1

2   1   4   3

3   4   1   2

1   2   3   4

Page 58 – Triple letters

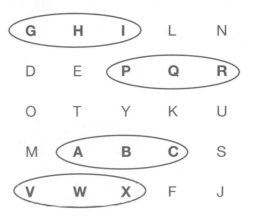

Page 59 – Tutti frutti

RASPBERRIES

Page 60 – Math quiz

```
0  0  1  5          9
                6  2  3  1
5  6  1  2          2     4
   2                1     6
   1  4  6  9             8
   4                     0
   5          8
         4  4  7  8
                0
4  6  7  8      0
```

Answers

Page 61 – Healthy mix

They are all vegetables

CARROTS   ONIONS   LEEKS

Page 62 – At the ballet

1. 3
2. 9
3. 5
4. 2
5. 4

Page 63 – Thirsty work

COFFEE

LEMONADE

SMOOTHIE

Page 64 – Who's this?

JAMES

Page 65 – Count to 55

50 + 5

40 + 15

30 + 25

35 + 20

37 + 18

Page 66 – Month mix up

OCTOBER

Page 67 – Square riddles

2	4	1	3
3	1	2	4
1	3	4	2
4	2	3	1

Page 68 – Letter puzzle

Q	M	N	O	W
P	D	E	F	C
R	I	G	A	V
S	T	U	H	Y
X	B	J	K	L

Page 69 – Snap, snap

CROCODILE

Answers

Page 70 – Nutty numbers

```
3 4 5 6         0
                2
  9 0 3 4       1   8
4       2       3   7
4 3 7 9             4
4       4           2
6       7   5
          8 3 4 0
          7
0 0 0 1     8
```

Page 71 – Money-go-round

They are all currencies

DOLLAR   POUND   EURO

Page 72 – Flowerpots

1. 1
2. 2
3. 2
4. 3
5. 3

Page 73 – Fruit bowl

BANANA

CHERRY

PEACH

Page 74 – Take out

PIZZA

Page 75 – Count to 60

30 + 30

40 + 20

50 + 10

45 + 15

42 + 18

Page 76 – Where in America?

CALIFORNIA

Answers

Page 77 – Funky figures

4	2	1	3
1	3	4	2
2	4	3	1
3	1	2	4

Page 78 – Alphabetical

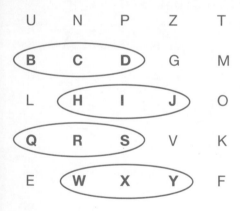

U	N	P	Z	T
B	C	D	G	M
L	H	I	J	O
Q	R	S	V	K
E	W	X	Y	F

Page 79 – All shook up!

MILKSHAKE

Page 80 – Number crunching

```
5 6 4 5          2
3                3
4                1
7          2 5 4 1
  8                  8
2 6 3 4              5
  7        3 6 9 1   6
  9                  0
      4 5 8 9
            8 9 6 7
```

Page 81 – Woody walk

They are all types of wood

OAK   PINE   BEECH

Page 82 – Something fishy

1. 4
2. 2
3. 3
4. 2
5. 2

Answers

Page 83 – What's the weather?

SNOWING

SUNNY

RAINING

Page 84 – Pick a color

GREEN

Page 85 – Count to 65

50 + 15

55 + 10

45 + 20

35 + 30

40 + 25

Page 86 – Over the sea

SEAGULL

Page 87 – Number grids

3	4	1	2
2	1	4	3
1	2	3	4
4	3	2	1

Page 88 – Secret letters

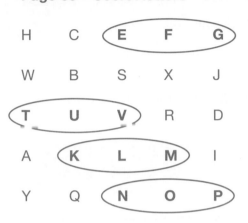

H	C	E	F	G
W	B	S	X	J
T	U	V	R	D
A	K	L	M	I
Y	Q	N	O	P

Page 89 – Going places

AIRPLANE

Page 90 – Find the numbers

```
5 7 6 8              3
      6 4 7 1        5
                     9
      2              5
5 6 3 4      7
      2      5
0 0 3 4      6
        5 2 3 1
0 3 4 1
        9 1 2 3
```

Answers

Page 91 – Yummy snacks

They are all fruit

PEAR   APPLE   BANANA

Page 92 – Funny faces

1. 6
2. 3
3. 2
4. 2
5. 1

Page 93 – Where am I from?

FRANCE

SPAIN

ENGLAND

Page 94 – Hard cheese

CHEDDAR

Page 95 – Count to 70

35 + 35

40 + 30

45 + 25

55 + 15

60 + 10

Page 96 – At the bakers

BAGUETTE

Page 97 – Tricky numbers

4	2	3	1
1	3	4	2
3	1	2	4
2	4	1	3

Page 98 – Chain letters

Y (C D E) T

G X (O P Q)

F N L Z H

(I J K) A S

B (U V W) M

Page 99 – In space

JUPITER

Answers

Page 100 – Silly sums

```
9 9 0 0
7 8 3 4          0
          2    3
    4 6 2 1    2    0
          2         0
8 1 1 2    1         3
                    4
        7 8 3 4

5 6 6 7      5 6 4 5
```

Page 101 – What's a foot?

They are all types of footwear

SNEAKER   BOOT   SHOE

Page 102 – Cat show

1. 3
2. 1
3. 1
4. 2
5. 4

Page 103 – Rainbow colors

BLUE

YELLOW

GREEN

Page 104 – Shiny stone

RUBY

Page 105 – Count to 80

40 + 40
70 + 10
60 + 20
50 + 30
65 + 15

Page 106 – Pussycat

PERSIAN

Answers

Page 107 – Number fun

3	2	1	4
1	4	3	2
2	1	4	3
4	3	2	1

Page 108 – Letter grid

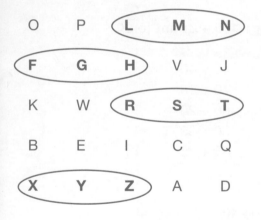

Page 109 – Giant of the sea

BLUE WHALE

Page 110 – Crack the code

```
6 6 7 8        9      9
               0      9
               8      9
      1 0 0 0        3
  7
  5 3 5 3 5
2 6            2 3 4 5
1 9
2              7 7 8 8
8   1 6 2 1
```

Page 111 – Tasty treat

They are all types of ice cream

RASPBERRY RIPPLE
TUTTI FRUTTI
CHOC CHIP

Page 112 – Monster parade

1. 3
2. 1
3. 2
4. 2
5. 3

Answers

Page 113 – Bird bonanza

FINCH
SPARROW
THRUSH

Page 114 – Sweet stuff

HONEY

Page 115 – Count to 90

45 + 45
80 + 10
60 + 30
50 + 40
65 + 25

Page 116 – On your head

BEEHIVE

Page 117 – Number squares

1	4	3	2
3	2	4	1
2	3	1	4
4	1	2	3

Page 118 – Letter square

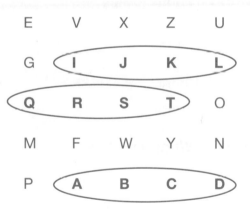

E   V   X   Z   U
G   I   J   K   L
Q   R   S   T   O
M   F   W   Y   N
P   A   B   C   D

Page 119 – Hot wheels

LIMOUSINE

Answers

Page 120 – What number?

```
6 7 6 7            7 2
                   8 7
4 6 4 5            3 7
                   4 7
5 7 3 9      2
         1 3 2 3
             1
3 5 4 5      0
           2 5 1 8
9 8 9 8
```

Page 121 – Funny felines

They are all types of cat

MANX   PERSIAN   SIAMESE

Page 122 – Wriggly reptiles

1. 4
2. 3
3. 5
4. 1
5. 2

Page 123 – Wild cats

PANTHER

LEOPARD

BOBCAT

Page 124 – Little waiter

PENGUIN

Page 125 – Count to 100

$$50 + 50$$
$$60 + 40$$
$$80 + 20$$
$$70 + 30$$
$$90 + 10$$

Page 126 – Hear the beat

ROCK AND ROLL

Page 127 – Four figures

```
3    2    4    1

1    4    3    2

4    1    2    3

2    3    1    4
```